Rabbit's Spring Gift

Anita Loughrey
Illustrated by Lucy Barnard

Rabbit's mum had been working hard all morning, spring cleaning their warren.

Rabbit was singing loudly. She was practising a song she had written for her mum, to say thank you.

Rabbit's brother covered his ears.
"Mum doesn't like songs," he said,
"she likes gifts, and I've got her the
best gift in the world to say thank you."

Rabbit stomped outside. “I’m going to get Mum a special gift too!” she said.

She hopped around
little puddles to
the vegetable plot
where new plants
were sprouting.

She rummaged in
the crocuses and
hunted in mole holes,
until she found
something perfect.

"Look what I've got you,
Mum," said Rabbit.

"Thank you, bobkin!
That's a perfect spring gift."

Mum gave her
a big smile.

Just then Rabbit's brother came crashing into the warren. "I've got you a spring flower, Mum," he said. "Thank you, munchkin!" beamed Mum.

Rabbit scowled at her brother. "My flower is better than yours," he sniggered.

Rabbit stomped outside.
“I’m going to find an even
better gift,” she said.

She peered into a pond full
of frogspawn. A newborn
chick twittered from a
nest above her head.

Rabbit searched through the gravel where ladybirds were waking after a long winter.

Then she spotted something tasty in the vegetable plot...

...a row of bright red radishes. She heaved one out of the ground and raced home as fast as she could.

"Look what I've got for you, Mum,"
Rabbit said brightly.

"Thank you, Rabbit.
What a tasty spring
treat!" said Mum.

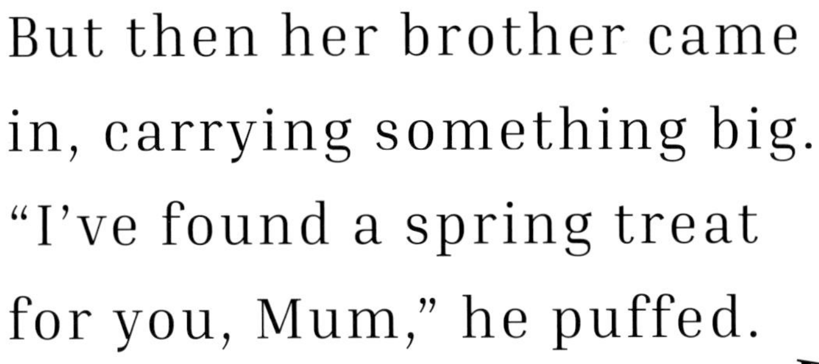

But then her brother came in, carrying something big. “I’ve found a spring treat for you, Mum,” he puffed.

“Gosh! That’s… lovely!” Mum said.

Rabbit scowled at her brother. Her back leg thumped at the ground.

Rabbit stomped back outside.
"I'm going to find the best
gift ever," she said.
She scrabbled through the
long grass and scuffled under
trees full of beautiful blossom.

She skipped past the
busy, buzzing bees
and the butterflies
fluttering around
the branches.

Then she saw it under the cherry
tree – a feather as white as a bobtail!
It was the perfect gift.

A gust of wind whisked the
feather up into the tree.
Rabbit bounced higher
and higher until...

"Got it!" she cried at last.
Rabbit tried to hop down,
but it was too high.

Her brother crept out from his hiding place, laughing. "It's all your fault," Rabbit said, as her brother helped her down from the branch. "You keep finding bigger and bigger gifts!"

But her brother just laughed and zoomed off.
“I’ve got something feathery for Mum too,”
he yelled over his shoulder.
Rabbit chased after him.

“This is for you, Mum,”
Rabbit’s brother said with a grin.

"Err! Thank you..."
said Mum.

Rabbit hid her feather behind her back.
“What have you got there, Rabbit?” asked Mum gently. Rabbit bowed her head and showed Mum the feather she had found.

Mum smiled. "What a beautiful feather.
I love both gifts, just like I love you both the same." She scooped them up in a big hug.
"And I don't need big or small gifts.

You are the best gifts of all!"

Spring Activities

Fun and simple ideas for you and your child to enjoy together.

Pond dipping

1. Take a net, a magnifying glass and a plastic container to your local pond.
2.Draw a figure of eight in the water with your net, keeping it close to the edge of the pond.
3. Turn the net inside out into the plastic container and use your magnifying glass to see what you have caught. You might see frogspawn, snails, dragonfly nymphs and other water insects.
4. Gently tip the creatures back into the water when you have finished.

Spring flower collage

Draw, colour, take photographs and print out pictures of spring flowers to make your own bright and colourful spring flower picture. How many different spring flowers can you name?

Grow your own

1. Save apple or orange pips from your food, or buy some seeds from a garden centre.
2. Plant them in a pot of soil and keep it on a windowsill.
3. Make sure it gets plenty of sunshine and water.
4. Pick, wash and taste your fruit and vegetables when they have grown in the summer.

'Signs-of-spring I spy'

Use the pages in this book or go for a spring walk with your child to play 'signs-of-spring I spy'. See what signs of spring you can spot. Say: "I spy with my little eye, a sign of spring beginning with the letter…". For example, you could use 'C' for crocus, 'F' for frogspawn or 'B' for blossom.

Did you spot the signs of spring in the story?

The cherry tree was full of beautiful blossom.

Blossom is a symbol of spring. Its strong smell attracts bees and other insects to pollinate the delicate flowers. Blossom only lasts for about two weeks before it starts to fall and then the fruit, such as cherries, begin to grow.

New plants were sprouting in the vegetable plot.

Most vegetables start to grow in the spring. Spring rain and warm sunshine help the seeds to grow. First the roots grow, then a shoot pushes its way through the soil to reach the sunlight. Leaves grow on the stem, then later, flowers and fruit will grow. Most fruit and vegetables are not ready to eat until summer or autumn, but some vegetables, such as radishes and cauliflowers, are harvested in spring.

Chicks were being born in their nests.

In spring, birds are busy collecting materials to build new nests to lay their eggs so new birds can be born. If you listen carefully, you can hear lots of different birds singing when spring is on the way. They sing to attract a mate or defend their territory. Many birds that migrated (flew to a warmer place) over winter also return home during spring.

The pond was full of frogspawn.

Frogs lay eggs called frogspawn in ponds during spring. The eggs are covered in jelly to protect them. The little black spots inside the jelly are the eggs. These eggs hatch into tadpoles. First the tadpole's back legs grow and then the front legs. When the tadpole has legs and still has a tail, it is called a froglet. As the froglet grows it loses its tail and becomes a frog.

Quarto is the authority on a wide range of topics.
Quarto educates, entertains and enriches the lives of our readers—enthusiasts and lovers of hands-on living.
www.quartoknows.com

Editor: Harriet Stone
Designer: Sarah Andrews & Victoria Kimonidou
Author: Anita Loughrey
Illustrator: Lucy Barnard

This edition first published in 2020 by QED Publishing, an imprint of The Quarto Group.
The Old Brewery, 6 Blundell Street, London N7 9BH, United Kingdom.
T (0)20 7700 6700 F (0)20 7700 8066
www.QuartoKnows.com

A catalogue record for this book is available from the British Library.

ISBN 978 0 7112 5081 9

Manufactured in Guangdong, China TT122019

9 8 7 6 5 4 3 2 1